Secrets of Dry Creek

SECRETS OF DRY CREEK

VERN HARRIS

"Secrets of Dry Creek" is a fictional novel, however
it is drawn from actual events and places.

Cover design by BookPOD
Typesetting by BookPOD

Printed and bound in Australia by BookPOD

ISBN: 978-0-6459193-0-1 (paperback)
eISBN: 978-0-6459193-1-8 (ebook)

NATIONAL LIBRARY OF AUSTRALIA

A catalogue record for this
book is available from the
National Library of Australia

CHAPTER 1

⟫⟫⟫⟩ • ⟨⟨⟨⟨⟨

As the sun set in a small community of Northern California the surrounding mountains sent an eerie but familiar feeling to Clint. It had been many decades since he returned to his homeland. A chill ran up and down his spine. Clint was now an old man and a strong sense of emotion arose as he stood and remembered those long ago years of his youth. Time had treated him well. A man now in his 70s, still physically fit with not many ailments at this time. Although this had not always been so.

When Clint was growing up in Stonyford in the 1940s to the 1960s, life was blissful and uncomplicated. A young man of Native American, Spanish and English descent, he loved to hunt, fish and enjoy the beauty that Stonyford provided.

Mother nature had blessed Stonyford with a natural geographical location. The surrounding mountains and two nearby creeks provided the local residents with ample farmland, fishing and harvesting areas. In the early years, a subsistence lifestyle existed. Clint could not have wished for more as he had shown natural instincts for providing game for his family's table.

He slowly assessed his memories from the past and wondered what to do next. Because Stonyford was not large, the main street had not changed. A small grocery store, Bar, Post Office and Café still existed. Almost the same as it was in the early days of his youth. He decided to walk to where his old wooden home once stood. He knew it was no longer there, but the old elm trees were still alive and growing where a new brick house now stood. Also there were the same beautiful Californian Poppies lapping the last rays of sunlight.

The poppies reappeared every year in Spring. They were a beautiful orange colour that created a continuous blanket-like effect in his parents' yard.

Memories – a long time ago, but still very vivid in Clints mind.

As none of his family were living in Stonyford he needed to find a place to stay for a few days. He stopped at the local grocery store and asked the owner if he could find accommodation for the night. The owner of the grocery store told him that there were two cabins a short way from town and he would probably be able to hire one for a couple of nights. He thanked her and drove towards Lake Wallan, remembering where it was located.

Lake Wallen was a reasonably large man-made lake that provided some tourism plus water storage for the larger towns east of Stonyford. Clint caught "Crappie" and Bass from the Lake, but he preferred to fish for the native rainbow trout in the nearby mountain streams.

He slowly climbed into his new 4x4 Jeep Pickup. A huge step forward from his ownership of a measly model Jeep in his youth. The two mile drive to the cabins was now asphalted and not the dirt road as he remembered it to be.

Digger pines and oak trees were still in abundance along the narrow road. Clint kept his eyesight on the road but was hopeful of seeing some wildlife. During his youth he probably would have seen quail, grey and ground squirrels, jackrabbits or even a few deer. Not now though. He could only spot a couple of ground squirrels. As the distance to the cabins was not far, Clint noticed a small road and turned left. Just a short way down the road the two cabins appeared, plus a larger home. The cabins were situated far enough apart to give a tenant privacy. They were not big, but comfortable enough for a short stay.

When he drove up to the house an older lady appeared at the front door and Clint got out of his Jeep and approached her. He immediately recognised her. Edith Bronson. She had been two years his senior at high school. Edith about fainted when she saw him. It had been over fifty odd years since Clint left Stonyford. He was amazed. She still looked the same, other than the grey hair, wrinkles and a limp when she strode over to him.

After all the greetings, Edith told Clint that she had married Virgil Marshall and had two children. The children had long moved out to the Sacramento Valley. Virgil had died five years before and she then purchased the cabins. After the quick 'catch up' Edith rented Clint one of the cabins. She gave him a discount of 20% and asked him to stay for supper that night. He declined, saying the next day would be better. That was fine with Edith.

Many memories swirled around in Clint's head that night. In the morning he climbed into his Jeep and decided to drive into Stonyford to see if anyone remembered him from the past. The little café was open, so he went in and ordered coffee and a small breakfast. No one else was in the café so he asked the young girl her name and if she was a local. Clint found out her name was Rose and she was the granddaughter of James and Lucy Williams. She said they were very elderly now and were "old timers" of the community. Rose told him that they lived just out of town near Baldy Creek. Clint said that he knew it well He paid, left the café and began to drive up the road that ran parallel to Baldy Creek. He started to follow the road and remembered it had its beginnings at Goat Mountain, a good two hours' drive away. Memories started to kick in, as this was where his father, (Clint Senior) used to drive down with the truck loaded with freshly sawn timber. It was more like a very narrow track than a road as Clint got near the end of it. Back in the early 1950s, there was a small timber mill located in an isolated valley near the top of Goat Mountain. The mill could only produce and process about one and a half loads of timber a day. He remembered the mill closing in the late 1950s. Clint and his brother Bill often rode with their dad during those early timber years. They would bounce around in the "Mack" lumber truck as it moved slowly down the narrow and steep gradient road. It always amazed them how their father could keep control of the speed of the truck by shifting to lower gears so that the brakes did not get too hot. He remembered one time how Bill had managed to sneak a small wad of tobacco from the "jockey box". Their father always kept a packet of tobacco there. Bill proceeded to chew it and needless to say became very ill, vomiting all over himself and the trucks interior. Their father eventually found a small flat area near a small spring running on the side of the road. He got Bill some water and cleaned him up. Some years later Bill told Clint he never chewed tobacco again. A lesson learned the hard way.

Clint found the mill was in disrepair and ramshackle state. It looked as though nobody had been there for years – which was probably very true. Clint just sat in the Jeep and reminisced for a while before driving back to Stonyford.

He could recall the mill only employed four full time workers. Only part of the mill had a covering over it and the rest was open. There was a sawyer, lumber stacker, and two men doing various odd jobs. Clints father knew the men as they were from the Stonyford area. It was hard work during the early days as they used mainly old worn-out machinery. The timber was cut from several small privately owned properties before it was sawn into lumber at the mill.

It was late afternoon when he arrived back in Stonyford. The Bar was open, so he went in for a late lunch and cold beer. He asked the bartender if there were any of the Indians still residing at the small Indian reservation known as the Rancheria. He was told there was only a handful of them, but they still lived there. One had to cross the bridge over the Baldy River then take a short drive to the base of Black Diamond Mountain. Clint used to drive to the Rancheria when he was a high school teenager to see his friends.

Joe Archenta and Bob Archenta were Native American people, known locally as Pomo Indians. They were brothers and both were Clints' friends and school mates at the Newville High School approximately 30 miles away. Clint had been a very good baseball pitcher in High School and Bob was his catcher. Joe played in the outfield. After a long school bus ride from Newville, the young men often donned hunting gear to set out and see what they could bring home for dinner. All three were very accurate marksmen. In those early days game was abundant and the young men usually brought home ample food to their respective families. As Clint drove up the bumpy road, he could see that the Rancheria was in serious disrepair. The main building was a 'board and bat' house. Many of the boards were askew and no paint applied. Pretty much as Clint remembered it. Upon his arrival he saw an elderly Indian woman standing in the doorway. Her appearance was weather-beaten, wrinkled, wearing glasses, grey haired, with a stooped posture. Clint still managed to recognise her immediately even after all the years that had passed. Again, as with Edith, his memory kicked in and he could see Joe and Bob's sister and he wondered "God how old must Harlene Archenta be!?"

Clint could see that Harlene did not recognise him. He climbed out of his Jeep and mouthed the word "Ho" to her, a Pomo greeting. As Clint looked her in the eyes he could see her wrinkled, weathered-worn face begin to shine somewhat. Harlene then said "Ho" also. "I know you, Clint. Welcome to the Archenta home. It will be like years gone by". 'Ho, Ho'. After small talk, Harlene and Clint sat with some coffee and a small bowl of venison stew.

Clint firstly asked if Fire Sticks Archenta was still alive. "No" Harlene said, "He died many years ago, a broken man, with a broken heart". Both his sons, Joe and Bob were killed in the Vietnam War. Of course Clint knew this, as he himself had spent two tours of duty there. Harlene said, "The boys and Fire Sticks are all buried in the back near the big oak tree", which she pointed out. Their mother Berlea Archenta had passed away about twenty-five years ago Harlene said, adding "I am always here with them, along with their spirits."

The word 'spirits' immediately resonated in Clints mind as this was one of the main reasons for him returning to the place of his youth. He stayed chatting for some time, but eventually relented and said goodbye. He did ask Harlene if he could come back and talk more. She said, "Yes Clint, you were always like one of the family."

He arrived back at the cabin at Lake Baldy and saw Edith at the front of her home. It was as if she was waiting for him to arrive. She waved and walked over to him. She asked, "How did your day go?" and if he was still coming to dinner. Clint said, "You betcha".

Later after dinner, Clint and Edith sat near an open fireplace on a couch that had seen better days. After a lot of small talk, Clint asked about many of the residents of Stonyford and what had become of them. Edith said that many had died or left the town. Only a handful were still around and a few of their children. However, Clint had not been friendly with the ones still there, except for the Archenta family. Edith told him she remembered him being friendly with the two Archenta boys and how sad it had been for the small community when learning of their deaths during the Vietnam conflict. Clint replied that he'd had some contact with the boys as they had meant so much to him in the earlier years of his life. They had been more like family and could always be trusted when he grew up in Stonyford.

Clint thanked Edith for dinner and for the information about past and present residents of Stonyford and retired to his cabin with much to think about.

CHAPTER 2

◆━━➤➤➤➤➤ ● ◀◀◀◀◀━━◆

Clint had been an avid hunter and fisherman as a young man, plus he loved the outdoors and the natural environment Mother Nature had created. Often, he would trudge along forest trails or river streams in his own little world. He knew this was a blessing and the solitude was something he cherished. When he found a pristine open glade or grassy knoll he would often just sit and listen to the forest sounds, breathe the earthy scent, or just observe all of the natural beauty that was on offer. The wind blowing through the trees, birds chirping or often silence. After rain there was a freshness that could be smelt in the air. In most cases his keen eyesight could correlate all aspects of a peaceful glade or if there was a danger lurking. Danger could be sensed when there were no birds singing, or if there were smells of dead animals. Clint felt his instinct came from his Paiute Indian heritage. He preferred the silence and serenity as it provided a calmness to his soul.

Hopefully no mechanized man-made inventions, cars or planes were nearby to interrupt during these serene times.

Many times Clint felt the need to know basically how the Indians had coped and survived in the wilderness before the 'white-man' had arrived. The Indians' way of life must have been challenging and difficult, but in a way that was different from the present.

Clint had found many abandoned temporary Indian camps or in a few cases larger more permanent camps while hunting. He had found many of these around the hinterland of Stonyford and the main mountain areas. One day he thought he would like to chart on a map the actual locations of some of the smaller camps. He knew no one else would ever find their location due to the terrain and remoteness of the land. A few camp sites he had found were now covered with chamise brush or other trees or bushes. Whenever he found something of importance, an artifact or signs of an ancient settlement, a strange feeling always overtook him. He did not know what this was, but through time and awareness it became more prevalent.

The signs that ancient Indian camps existed varied from large to small. Large villages had areas set aside for chipping arrowheads, spear heads, hide scraping stones and knives. Sometimes grinding rocks that squaws used for preparing food could be found. The smaller camps were harder to locate as they were often overgrown with brush and other vegetation. Obsidian chips, scattered animal bones, or old fire pits might be present, but not always visible. Whether they be large or small encampments, they were near water holes or streams. Clints Indian heritage and instinct, along with many hunting and fishing trips, were of great advantage when scouting for signs.

His awareness and feelings associated with the old Indian encampments were sacred to his psyche as they represented something that was connected to his people's past. Possibly, these were the beginnings of the Spirits awakening within him.

Dreams Valley was really a large series of rolling hills with an abundance of black oak trees growing on them. A few small man-made dams were in sections of the Valley. They were used for watering cattle and wild animals. Acorns fell from the oak trees during late Summer and Autumn. This was the season when the deer migrated off the higher mountains. The deer ate the acorns and became fat and healthy, making them prime targets for hunters.

On one particular day, Clint and Joe Archenta had walked quite a few miles into this area searching for a nice buck to kill and take back to their respective families. They had been traversing up a ridgeline when suddenly a buck and two does darted across in front of them. Clint, who saw the deer first, threw his rifle to his shoulder and fired one quick shot. Joe did not have time to shoot as the deer were gone in a flash. Back in the early days the young men only had 'peep' or open sights. If they had a scope no shot would have been fired. Clint said, "Even though I don't know if I hit the buck, we better go and see." Off they went to have a look. Joe was first to see a small spot of blood on the ground. He said, "Looks as though you hit the buck". Sure enough, the spots of blood grew larger and more liquid. They both followed the sign of blood to a small thicket of brush. Clint said, "Look", and there on top of the brush was a nice three-point antlered buck. The buck must have made one last bound and fell dead in the thick brush.

When they dragged the buck out and started to gut it, they noticed it had been shot through the heart. The heart and liver were always a delicacy to eat, but in this particular deer they were going to have to throw the heart away. Clint and Joe prepared the buck into a 'backpack'. They did this by breaking the front legs and skinning a strap of hide down and then cutting a hole through the hind leg joints. This allowed the front and hind legs to be attached together, similar to the straps on a backpack. When they finally completed this Clint got under the deer carcass and shouldered it on to his back. As it was a good-sized buck it made him wobble until he got used to the extra weight. They decided to go back to the main road via Dry Creek because it was flatter and easier to walk.

Dry Creek, as the name suggests, most of the time had no or very little water in it. When Clint and Joe finally reached the creek bed they had a short rest and a drink of water from the containers they carried attached to their belts. They were at the head of the creek bed and it was fairly steep. Clint was exhausted packing the three-point buck, so they changed over and Joe got the job. Packing a good-sized buck on a man's back was not an easy task. Keeping one's balance and the extra weight when walking down the uneven terrain, such as large and small stones was quite difficult. Even though Clint and Joe were extremely fit, they had trouble at times. The buck on their backs created a problem of blood on their skin and ticks attaching to their bodies. They would check for ticks when taking showers when they returned to Stonyford.

The two friends started slowly down the creek bed and the further they made their way out, the path became slowly wider and not so steep. Very little was said as the two young men proceeded. Clint, always noticing any unusual objects said to Joe, "I've noticed a few obsidian chips." Obsidian being the rock or stone Indians used to make arrowheads and start fires. Joe said nothing and continued his slow and cautious walk, carrying the deer. In places, they had to manoeuvre around a lot of boulders. As they walked, Clint began to feel a strange or odd sensation that there was someone or something very near. It was a very strong feeling and because Clint was slowing down Joe decided to take a break to see what was ailing him. Where they actually paused, there was a flatter and wider area with another flat area just above the old water course. They went up the bank and sat down resting and again drinking water.

Clint was becoming very puzzled as he had been imagining that there were others in the area where they were resting.

Joe did not have this strange feeling, but said to Clint, "Look at the ground there", pointing at the ground just in front of where they were sitting. It was unusual, as the ground had been sunken in rectangles, as if there were two graves, side by side. It was clear that the sunken areas had been there for a long time. Both young men did not know what to make of these unusual depressions. Clint, however, was getting more and more of a strange sensation of another presence and it seemed to be coming from the two depressions in the ground. Joe however was not getting this odd sensation. Clint decided to lie down for a short time and as he did so visions began to take form in his mind. He began to visualise two Indians. They resembled young women with long black hair and wearing buckskin clothes. They seemed to be in their early twenties. Clint sensed that this was a sign and that they were somehow the spirits from the newly discovered graves. He felt connected with these signs as there was a strange energy being transmitted into his body. Joe asked Clint what was going on and Clint tried to explain what he believed he visualised, and that was all. Joe did not know what to think of this and simply said, "It's best that we keep moving and away from this spot." Clint agreed and off they went.

As they continued to carry the three-point buck, Clint felt other accompanying sensations until they got to their vehicle and headed back to their homes in Stonyford.

Neither Clint nor Joe spoke anymore about this experience. Joe seemed to forget about it, but Clint somehow could never keep it from bothering him and it was always in the back of his mind.

As he developed into manhood Clint wondered if the energy and signs would continue to emerge from what he believed to be two female spirits.

CHAPTER 3

Time took over and the years moved on. Clint grew older and his athletic prowess was noticed by colleges and universities in California. He was an above average basketball player and an exceptional baseball pitcher. During their High School days Clint, Joe and Bob Archenta were very close and a strong bond developed between them. Their hunting and fishing trips maintained this unique relationship. Bob was the quiet one, but Clint and Joe often talked about the future, jobs, schooling and of course, girls.

Joe and Bob were not especially fond of school and were keen on getting a job after High School. However, there were not many jobs available in Stonyford nor the surrounding communities. Both Joe and Bob got seasonal work on local farms, mainly hay hauling and cattle farming work. It was usually physical work and the young men enjoyed doing it. It gave them a sufficient income and a sense of independence. They still lived on the Rancheria and paid their Mom and Dad board, plus provided meat for the table.

Clint on the other hand continued his education as a couple of Universities wanted him to play baseball for them. This was going to be a huge undertaking for him as he had always attended much smaller schools. One particular University could not give Clint a scholarship but offered him a few menial jobs. He did not have enough money so had to work at summer jobs as a 'logger'. His parents did not have enough money to pay his way to University or even to give him a small amount to help. Luckily, Clint's dad, had always worked in the timber industry and was able to get him a job as a 'knot bumper'. A knot bumper cut off all the knots when the logs were skidded onto the landing. From there the logs were put into stacks or log decks, until it was time to be loaded onto the logging trucks and carted to a huge sawmill near Stonyford. Clint's dad often gave him a ride to the mountains where he worked. Clint Snr was a log truck driver through a span of seven to eight years. Clint worked every summer logging. Always for the same "Gypo" logging company. Clints boss was a fantastic man and his family always looked after him.

Through the years, while logging Clint lived with his boss in a trailer house in the mountains. Clayton, the logging boss, let Clint start loading the log trucks with a 977 CAT track loader. It was not as physical, but he had to think to be able to load the logs so they fitted properly on the trucks. This was not always easy as the logs were of varying size and not always available on the landing where the trucks were being loaded.

As Clint only worked as a logger in the woods during the summer months, he had plenty of time to let his mind wander and think of the future. Usually, he worked only until around 3:00pm or 4:00pm, depending on how hot it was in the woods.

Several times during the summer months the loggers had to stop work early due to the 'Hoot Owl'. 'Hoot Owl' meant that a certain temperature had been reached and the Forest Service would stop work due to the extreme fire danger. As the workday was shortened considerably, Clint had a lot of time to himself. Often he would take short walks to explore and think of things that might eventuate in his future years.

Many things passed through Clints inquisitive mind with the main one being: What would be the outcome of his lifetime? Clint knew that only time would tell.

He still had those mysterious feelings he first came across when walking out of the woods with the buck he had shot. Sometimes they were helpful and comforting. He felt the need to rely on the presence of the spirits as they always transmitted an energy and released guidance when necessary. He now accepted them as some strange but non-threatening presence from his hunting trip with Joe.

Clint could remember vividly on one occasion after working all day 'knot bumping' he was extremely tired. On this occasion he had dinner, washed up and decided to go to bed early. He was living or 'batching' in a tent by himself on 'Sheet Iron Mountain'. One evening, before crawling into his sleeping bag he decided to relieve himself outside, 'as one does in the mountains'. He noticed it was an extremely clear night with the stars shining brightly. He then went back to the tent and immediately went to sleep. During the middle of the night he awoke with a bit of a fright. Clint was a light sleeper. Something was telling him to have a look outside the tent. As he peered over at another tent not far away, where two timber-fellers often stayed, he observed something very scary and strange. 'Spirits' almost immediately began to caution Clint. Why? Clint knew the two timber-fellers where not present this particular night. What was threatening him? Clint could make out two shadows. Like strange people.

The next day Clint asked some of his fellow loggers if they had seen or heard anything during the night. All said, "No never seen or heard a thing." Clint felt very strange and wondered if he was going around the twist. No more was mentioned of Clints 'strange people', but he every so often thought of the experience through his lifelong years. Clint knew the 'Spirits' knew, but never mentioned it either.

Early on during his logging years, Clint lived with a full blood Native American. Sharkey. The Indian lived in a small tent and Clint slept outside on a stretch canvas bed. This was quite adequate for him until in the early Spring when black bears with their cubs started to become a nuisance. The campsite was near a small stream and the bears started to come down the side of the mountain to drink. Often Clint would hear the black bears near his bed in the middle of the night which made him quite nervous and wary until they decided to move on. As he stayed awake most of the night, he awoke very tired. The bears never seemed to bother Sharkey as he was a sound sleeper.

Things changed a few weeks later as Sharkey and Clint returned to camp after their weekly trip off the mountain to get supplies and freshly washed clothes. The campsite was completely wrecked by bears when they arrived. Tins of food had been ripped open by the bears teeth, the tent and bed had been torn and ripped. All in all, most of their personal items had been destroyed. From then on Clint also started living in a tent and most personal items he kept in sturdy boxes. Clint believed the Spirits had a sense of humour as he felt a sign of amusement from the outcome of the bears destroying his campsite. Usually the Spirits were mostly concerned with his welfare.

Clint grew into a man during his time spent being a logger. Hard work was involved with not a lot of stress involved. He became extremely fit and enjoyed working in an environment without all the interventions of busy town to city life. No one to hassle him, just mostly peace and serenity. But things could change, and it did one day when he had advanced to becoming an operator of the 977 Cat track layer log loader. Clint had actually learned to operate the loader by himself when no one else was around. Once his boss Ron knew Clint could operate the machine that was it! Clint became the loader operator. Most times it was something Clint enjoyed as he had to figure out how to stack the logs on the log trucks in a way to make them fit properly. Sometimes the truck drivers would get angry if he did not give them all the good logs without the 'rot' in the timber. But this was not always possible. On one occasion a truck driver named Eric became highly agitated and demanded Clint to climb down from the loader. As he did Eric hit Clint from behind and knocked him to the ground. A fracas between the two men ensued leaving both bloodied and bruised. Ron soon arrived and broke up the fight and gave Eric his 'marching orders'. Clint was shaken and noticed that his right hand was starting to swell. Ron, the boss told Clint to drive down the mountain to the town that had a small hospital.

By the time Clint had driven the manual shift Pickup down to the township of Ponderosa his hand was throbbing. It was a wonder he had not passed out due to the pain. Luckily, he had dodged all the log trucks coming up the hill. The Doctors said his right hand was badly crushed and broken and would need an operation when the swelling went down. As it was Friday, and two fellow workmen were going back to Stonyford they picked him up from the Ponderosa Hospital. Clint was out of action for the rest of the logging season. The State Compensation gave him a payout of $4000. This was exceptionally good for the late 1960s.

It wasn't long after that Clint got a call from one of his University fellow baseball players. Roger Goldy was one of Clints best friends. He originally lived in Santa Clara before doing his University studies in Chico, California. They had been 'roomies' and also played baseball on the University team at Chico. Roger knew that Clint was a 'wanderlust' and thought he would like to travel throughout Europe with him, as Clint could not work.

CHAPTER 4

⊱━━━━⊰

A trip through Europe! Clint jumped at the chance to travel and especially to somewhere new. He would defer University at Chico for a year and travel. Roger arranged all the tickets and travel arrangements. All Clint would have to do was show up to Los Angeles, California, and board the plane to Weisbaden, Germany.

A small hinderance almost gave Clint second thoughts about travelling to Europe. About three weeks before he was to travel he decided to go trout fishing with his hometown Stonyford friend, Joe Archenta. They had driven to a stream near the High Plains of Goat Mountain. They had a great fishing trip and both caught their limit of ten trout. It was a small stream and they had to walk quite some way to catch the trout. Both of the young men of course gave their fish to their respective families. Clint noticed that an irritation had started to appear on his arms and inner thighs. He soon realised that Joe and he had both been in contact with poison oak bushes when fishing. The poison oak had not affected Joe, but unfortunately Clint was highly allergic to it. "Thank God", Clint thought when he found out what had caused the rash, as it was not contagious and he could still make the trip to Europe.

When Roger and Clint arrived at the airport in Frankfurt, all was alright. Just some inconvenience to Clint for about two weeks and then the itching and rash finally ceased. His right hand had a cast on it where it had been operated on, but didn't cause him too much discomfort. Clint and Roger decided that they would hire a car. As it turned out Clint knew a U.S. soldier, known as Monty. Monty had gone to school at a nearby town of Stonyford and he had played sport against him in High School. Clint knew this ahead of time and contacted him before leaving California. On arrival to Frankfurt Clint made a phone call to Monty and he was kind enough to give them a place to stay for just over a week. Clint had a great time catching up with Monty and his wife Ruth. Roger fitted in well also. During their short stay Monty showed the two men some of the local sites.

Monty arranged for them to hire a Volkswagon combi van for six weeks from another soldier. Very handy indeed, Clint and Roger both agreed and both had procured International Drivers Licences before leaving the U.S.

After a great stay with Monty and his wife Ruth, off they went, heading firstly to Italy. All they had was a tent, gas burner, one small pot, and cups; they were basically back-packing throughout Europe. This was all a new experience for both men as they were very excited and on a new adventure. A lot of incidents happened while driving on the opposite side of the road. This was quite common, but both Clint and Roger adapted well.

Most campsites were very cheap, but many did not have hot water for showers. It was a neat experience and they met many new friends. Mostly young women travelling and back packing.

The combi van was very handy and did not use much fuel. The only trouble they had was when they crossed the Alps entering Italy. Just before they reached the top and also downhill into Italy, the combi ceased to run properly, and in some cases stalled completely! Roger was very handy with mechanical issues and located the problem. Due to the high altitude the fuel line had formed a 'vapour lock' due to the low air pressure and freezing air.

Roger was a handsome man and had no problems meeting young women. Clint was somewhat shy and had a difficult time meeting the girls. However, as time passed on their journey throughout Europe the two young men always met girls and had many enjoyable times.

When Clint and Roger returned to the States after their experience abroad, things changed for both of them. Clint decided to go back to logging and Roger returned to his trade of shoeing horses.

Clint also decided to start a 'Uni' Course in the Redwoods forest region. The University was quite small and Clint knew he could get part-time work to pay for his schooling. He had many friends at the University. He even started playing baseball there as he was a very good pitcher. Time flew by and during his fourth and final year he fell in love with a very attractive woman. Clint was studying to become a teacher at University and needed to pick up some credits before finishing his final year. This was accomplished by applying to be a 'Teachers Aide' at the nearby town of Pacific. He got the job of helping with Primary School children and he received a nominal wage. He did this for three days a week when he did not have classes. He often did Aide work in the classroom for a young female teacher. Her name was Vickie Majoras and she was slender, blonde and an extremely gifted teacher. Clint assisted her troublesome children in the classroom.

Clint became very attracted to Vickie and one day became very bold and asked her if she wanted to go to the movies one weekend. He was 'ecstatic' as she said "yes". That was it, from then on almost every weekend they dated and had a special relationship. Many of her fellow teachers did not approve of the relationship due to an age difference, Clint was somewhat younger in age.

On a couple of occasions Clint drove all the way to Stonyford to visit his parents. Vickie had a very snazzy car, a blue Mustang, and Clint liked to drive it. It was a much nicer car than his 1957 blue Chevy. His Mom and Dad always tried to push his relationship with Vickie as they really liked her and thought he should marry her. This made him rebel somewhat as he liked to make his own decisions. Clint and Vickie's romance blossomed and they were becoming inseparable. Because the University in the Redwoods was located on the Northern Coast of California they spent a lot of weekends clamming, walking on the beaches and attending beach parties. Just before Clint was ready to graduate though, things were thrown into disarray. It was also at this time he had strange feelings of his life being altered dramatically. Clint knew there was a war in Vietnam and the Spirits were attempting to prepare him for the worst possible scenario. Going to war! Clints mind was confused and in turmoil.

Vickie noticed a change in Clint as he was not the same person and was becoming less approachable and caring. She kept asking Clint "what's wrong?" He had no answers. Everything changed in Clints life not long after this.

The dramatic change came about when he received a letter in the mail from the U.S. Government. Due to the major conflict in Vietnam during this time, Clint got the dreaded 'Greetings from Uncle Sam'. He was being conscripted into the Armed Services in about a months' time. He had just enough time to finalise all of his personal dealings before being inducted at Oakland California. Clint now realised the 'Spirits' were trying to prepare him for his unexpected future.

He hated to say his farewells to Vickie as he knew she cared for him a lot.

When he arrived at Oakland California he was immediately shipped to Ft. Lewis, Washington to complete his basic training. It was in the mid-1960s and Clint had to deal with several 'hippies' that also had been drafted. He was able to survive his eight weeks of basic training without too much trouble. He was very fit from his logging work and he did not mind all of the physical training that was required to be a good soldier. At the end of the eight week cycle, Vickie arrived at Ft. Lewis along with his Mother and Father. Although they got to see the graduation ceremony, Clint only saw them briefly before being sent straight to Ft. Gordon, Georgia to start eight weeks of Advanced Individual Training. He could not believe he was going to become a Military Policeman. Again, Clint acquitted himself well and completed the eight weeks without too much trouble.

While at Ft. Gordon he met up with Roger, his travelling friend, who had been inducted into the Army around the same time as Clint. As Clints Company C was about to be assigned, the Spirits tried to instil upon him the value of life, however this was not the case in Vietnam as life was not always valued. Clint would try his best to follow this advice as he knew there would be times when he would have to be valiant to ensure his own preservation.

Company C was being sent to Vietnam as replacement soldiers to keep the numbers up. This was required as so many young soldiers were either being wounded or killed in the mid 1960s.

Roger was in another Company and they were also eventually going to "Nam". Clint and Roger were able to meet briefly and vowed to meet in "Nam" if possible.

Clint was given a two week pass to visit his family in Stonyford. He had to stay overnight in a Hotel near the Atlanta, Georgia airport. He almost did not make his flight the next morning as he met a very attractive stewardess who had to stay overnight also. The next morning Clint barely made his flight as he and the sexy flight stewardess made love all night. "Oh my God," Clint thought. "I am worn out!" Sensations of happiness and amusement were passed into Clints psyche, approving of his zealous release of physical pleasure.

The two weeks leave from the Army seemed to go by very quickly. Clint visited many old friends from the Stonyford community and Vickie even got to make the long journey to Stonyford. She could only stay four days, but it was time well spent. Clint wanted to make love to Vickie, but she shunned his advances.

She would only agree to his sexual advances if they were to get married.

Clint could not agree to marriage as the commitment of going to a war zone weighed on his mind. This left Vickie an emotional wreck as she truly wanted to get married. When it came time to leave Stonyford, Vickie was totally emotionally confused, as was Clint. He was hoping the 'Spirits' would give him some advice, but none was forthcoming.

Just before Clint left to go to Oakland Army Terminal and leave for Vietnam, he wrote Vickie a long letter. It was one of the hardest things he had ever done. In the last letter he ever wrote to Vickie he wrote and made up a false story of him having met another woman and falling in love with her. He also said that they should not correspond again as it would only cause both of them heartache. It took ages for Clint to send the letter to Vickie. She replied that she never wanted to see Clint again, full stop. The only reason Clint had written what he did was because he had a strong feeling he would be killed in Vietnam and did not want her to have to wait for a dead or wounded soldier. This was so gut wrenching for Clint, but he did what he thought was right.

CHAPTER 5

Clint arrived in Bien Hoa, Vietnam on a commercial plane loaded with U.S Soldiers, or as they were called, FNGs! (Fucking New Guys). As they disembarked from the Tiger Airways aircraft they felt the extreme humidity hit them, almost taking their breath away. When the soldiers looked down from the Aircrafts gangway they could see many green 'body' bags of dead soldiers being transported back to the U.S. on the same plane they had arrived on.

It was a solemn sight and it really hit the soldiers hard. They knew they were in for the real deal. Clint and the other soldiers were loaded into trucks resembling cattle cars and were whisked away from Bien Hoa towards a Replacement Centre. That short trip was scary as there was a lot of artillery fire going on around them.

Welcome to Vietnam!

At the Replacement Centre all new soldiers were given orders as to the location they were going to and what Army units they would be assigned to. A lot of the new soldiers were going to infantry units. Clint was assigned to an MP Platoon attached to an infantry unit near a large Army base and small Vietnamese village.

Vietnam presented many dangers to Clint and other soldiers. On occasions a mysterious energy would be felt by him. He was aware this represented a sign by the Spirits to be careful and not to be too fervent with his actions.

He became very aware of these signs and followed them wherever he was while in Vietnam. Many of his Army buddies thought he was very lucky. Clint was originally posted to a very small Military Police Platoon as just a regular Military Police (MP) soldier. This was not the case for long as the Provost Marshall Major Lucky could see that he was not the average soldier and often acquitted himself well on many occasions when confronted with challenging situations.

Major Lucky witnessed many instances of this. Very early on while attending a violent clash of black vs white soldier standdown incident, Clint managed to control the two groups diplomatically even though the conflicting groups were high on either drugs or alcohol. The Spirits had transmitted a feeling of peaceful energy to Clint even though he was still very tense and alert. Clint took notice of the mysterious signs and managed to separate the two main groups, disarm the ringleaders, and apprehend them and put them into a cell consisting of two metal shipping containers. After interviewing the separate groups, it was clear that the whole incident revolved around racial conflict.

Due to Clint's diplomatic intervention and subsequent follow-up, he resolved the incident by peaceful negotiations. As the 'Spirits' whispered to Clint, "A huge feather in your hat or in this case, helmet". This made Clint very pleased, and he often chuckled to himself.

On another occasion Clint volunteered to be a M-60 machine gunman on a retrieval mission further north of the main base into the Michelin rubber plantations. On numerous occasions the M.P. Platoon had to lead convoys for all sorts of reasons. Clint's M-60 machinegun was mounted on a Jeep. The Jeep's in "Nam" usually had a metal piece of steel welded into the centre of the front chassis. The metal piece would be the first to hook onto a 'booby trap' that was usually a piece of barbed wire that was strung across a track at head height. The reason Clint decided to volunteer was to do something different from writing reports. It was a small convoy with only three vehicles, two jeeps front and back and a two and a half tonne tow truck. The convoys mission was to retrieve a two and a half tonne truck that had been badly damaged by a road mine. The truck had been carrying many Vietnam workers. Several had been wounded or killed. The driver of the truck, a US soldier, had also been killed. It was a scary operation for Clint as the perimeter was in disrepair and overgrown with all sorts of vegetation. When the convoy arrived at the destination the area was secured by several US soldiers. Two had German Shepherd dogs. This was a real eye opener for Clint and made him more aware of the many different things that could be encountered in a War Zone. The convoy itself escaped with no intervention, but Clint could hear a huge amount of combat activity taking place further into the Michelin Plantation. At one point two medivac helicopters flew low over them, evidently on a mission to evacuate dead or wounded soldiers. Clint finally relaxed as the convoy neared their main base.

About seven months into Clints tour of duty, a 'chopper pilot' from another region brought a note to him. It was from his childhood and school friend Joe Archenta. Joe was at 'Bear Cat' north of Clints location. Clint asked Major Lucky if it would be possible to hitch a chopper ride to 'Bear Cat'. Major Lucky was dubious but said he would try. Two days later Major Lucky approached Clint grinning ear to ear. He told Clint, "Be ready in three hours as you have your ride to Bear Cat." Clint could not believe what he heard!

That evening Clint was at a small Fire Support Base with Joe. It had been five months since they had last seen each other.

Clint and Joe spent the entire time talking about everything from past to present time. Joe was doing it tough as he had faced danger constantly. The particular Fire Support Base was in a vulnerable spot and was under some sort of enemy harassment constantly. Joe told Clint that his platoon had to go into the surrounding jungles frequently on patrol in search of enemy soldiers, that is the Vietnam Cong.

Before Clint was about to leave on a re-supply Chopper, they made a pact to see one another again in Stonyford and go hunting and fishing like old times. Of course, both knew that it would probably never eventuate. Clint had a strange feeling that he would never see Joe alive again. As the chopper made a half circle around the FSB, Clint felt an uneasiness and had shivers running up and down his spine. As he grew older, he could remember seeing Joe waving to him from below as the chopper headed back towards his own location near Bien Hoa. It was about two months later that Clint got word that Joe had been mortally wounded while on a search and destroy mission. The news about Joe affected Clint immensely and made him think about how precious life was. For the rest of Clints life he valued friendship and respected other people's attitudes towards living. The spirits kept reminding Clint that the world goes on and to love and respect others.

While in Vietnam the days seemed to go on in time at a slow pace. Very seldom did he have time to himself to enjoy. Clint enjoyed receiving mail from family and university friends. After about seven months he was granted R & R. Clint had several different countries to choose from, but eventually settled on taking his R & R in Australia. He wanted to see the Australian countryside, plus the young ladies he had heard about from other soldiers who had returned from their own R & R.

A M.P. Jeep took Clint to Saigon where he boarded a jet at Tan Son Nhut Airport. As Clint sat on the jet, excitement was building in anticipation of leaving the war in Vietnam to having a peaceful time in Australia.

The plane eventually made a fuel stop in Darwin, Australia. The soldiers had their first taste of 'Aussie' beer. Great! After taking off from Darwin they landed at their final destination, Sydney. Clint enjoyed seven days of bliss. Seeing the local sights and spending time with the young Aussie girls made Clint and other soldiers forget the war was even going on. Eventually however, all the good times had to come to an end. A flight back to Tan Son Nhut Airpot in Saigon with the sound of artillery in the distance made him realise the war was still in full swing.

Clint learned much about Military Justice and was keen to expand his knowledge about Military Law. Major Lucky took notice of Clints ability to work in Vietnam, he was promoted to a Specialist 5th Class. Basically, the same as a Sergeants rank. As his tour of duty was coming to close, Major Lucky allowed Clint to become his driver. For Clint this was a very easy task driving a jeep, plus he got out of the PMO (Provost Marshalls Office) and see some of the countryside in Southern Vietnam. One of his final assignments was to help with the security for one of Bob Hope's shows. Not only was this a great show, but opened Clints eyes to what was in store when he returned stateside as a civilian again. All the freedom to do what he wanted without the constraints of military life. Clint had become so accustomed to life as a soldier in Vietnam that he was actually contemplating 're-upping' and applying for another tour of duty.

He did not know whether he could go back to the U.S.A. and become a civilian. He had become used to the daily regimented life in Vietnam. Having not spoken to American women for over fourteen months the thought of doing so was awesome but also a daunting experience. Some of the Vietnam civilians were extremely beautiful and friendly people. They had become part of Clints life and were going to be hard to part company with. Finally though, he made the decision to leave Vietnam and begin a new life and prepare for the future.

On Clints last 3 days in Vietnam all equipment he had been given by the Army was returned and signed for. Even his rifle (M-16) and his Colt 45 revolver. He actually felt naked without a weapon as he sat and slept on a concrete slab waiting to hear his name read out on a flight manifest. He had many 'dreams' appearing during these lonesome days and nights. Many of these dreams had to do with new beginnings and the future. These dreams made Clint very apprehensive and melancholy at the same time. Finally, Clints name was called out from a manifest and he boarded on a 'Stretch' 704 Jet bound for the U.S.A. HOME!

As things panned out the flight seemed doomed as the plane was over boarded with GIs and when it began take off things were shaking and it took forever to reach the end of the runway at Bien Hoa Airport. There were too many troops aboard which almost caused a catastrophe. As Clint looked down at the end of the runway the 704 Jet barely made it off the ground. All the troops aboard were somewhat shaken from the ordeal and let out the biggest roar. All were thankful they were homeward bound.

CHAPTER 6

◦➤➤➤➤➤➤➤ ◆ ⫷⫷⫷⫷⫷⫷⫷◦

Clints yearning to return back to his hometown of Stonyford brought with it a lifetime of memories. The memories, plus the two 'Spirits' that had been with him everywhere he went since that day they had entered his world and being. Between the Spirits and himself he knew old age was well and truly upon him. For Clint there needed to be some reason why the Spirits had guided him and was a source of physical and mental protection. He decided he needed to walk back up Dry Creek where Joe and he had found the two burial sites. He thought if he did this, that possibly the Spirits might leave his soul and return to their original resting place. Before this could happen, Clint would need to get permission from the new landowners of the land encompassing Dry Creek and the graves. Again, he decided to ask Edith who they were. Edith was quite willing to oblige Clint and said that a middle aged couple had bought the ranch many years ago after Clint had left Stonyford on his adventures of the world. Edith said that John and Helen Adamson were very nice and a credit to the local Stonyford community. They had fitted in well and were an asset when the locals required assistance. Edith said John and Helen had provided a place to shelter and to feed after the devastating fires of 2005. Clint asked Edith if she thought they would speak to him and possibly give him permission to enter their private land to investigate the burial site. She said they more than likely would, but would not allow hunting as they were very protective of the natural animal and vegetation life.

Edith gave the owners of the Dry Creek region a call and asked, if Clint could visit them. Sure enough they said, Clint could visit them for lunch on a Thursday.

John and Helen were waiting for Clint when he arrived at their Ranch, which they had named the Dry Creek Ranch. After a quick tour they sat down at a table for a typical Stonyford lunch. Chilli Beans and Corn Bread.

As their conversation turned to the access of the Dry Creek area near and below the Mountain Black Diamond, Clint mentioned that he knew of a lot of Indian campsites of time gone by. John and Helen were very interested as they did not realise there were several Indian camps in the Dry Creek region. Clint mentioned, that he had found some arrowheads and grinding stones in the area when he was a young man. Eventually he mentioned the two graves and the mystery about them. He related how the 'Spirits' had been with him ever since that time Joe Archenta had laid the buck down to have a breather and rest. John and Helen became more attentive when Clint mentioned his visions of the two Indian maidens. That's when an historical story began to unfold and John and Helen began to relate some of the stories they had heard from some of the old-timers and historians of Stonyford.

John and Helen began to retell the story to Clint as 'Harry Hub' a local Indian elder had told them and others in the community of Stonyford. The story on folklore of the local Native Indians had been passed on and on and was based on fact.

The story began and took place before the 'white man' had arrived. Stonyford was not a town yet and the area around the main Stonyford Creek was mainly occupied by the local Indians belonging to the Pomo Nation. They were basically hunters and gatherers. They were not considered a war-like tribe and therefore traded with other Indian tribes, especially those from the west coast for items and material they did not have.

The coastal Indians basically traded seashells and some hides to the Pomo's, plus there was a mountain called 'Kelso Mountain' that was a volcanic glass mountain, or Obsidian. Of course, the obsidian was what all Indians used to chip arrowheads or make axes. There was also a belief that the obsidian was a source of healing powers and energy, therefore, it was highly valued by the Indians.

The Pomo Indians traded acorns, arrowheads, trinkets and mainly salt to the coastal tribes. Luckily for the Pomo's there were several small salt flats and one very large salt flat. The squaws of the Pomos would gather large amounts of the salt and have it ready for when the coastal Indians arrived and started trading.

Hardly ever was there any bickering or fighting with the coastal Indians. However, as history has it, on one particular occasion, there had been a small uprising between them. A group of coastal Indians arrived at the Stonyford region. They were mainly young braves and were looking not only for salt but for Pomo squaw maidens. They were a fierce group and decided to take a few of the young squaws for their own satisfaction. According to legend, one thing led to another and a fight ensued. Eventually, several young squaws were taken by force and without consent from local Pomo elders. Several of the coastal braves were killed. About twelve coastal braves escaped, but they had captured two of the young maiden squaws. These two squaws were the daughters of Sharkill, the Chief of the Pomo tribe. They were only eighteen and twenty years old. Both were Princesses and were very pretty. These two Princesses were never seen or heard of again. Chief Sharkill amassed several Pomo braves and tracked down and killed the maverick group of young coastal braves. The saddest part of the legend was that neither of the two Princesses were ever found. Chief Sharkill never let the coastal Indians return to the Stonyford Indian lands and eventually traded with other Indians further afield. Chief Sharkill died a fairly young Indian, only about fifty years old. Evidently, he and his wife died of broken hearts. As time passed on there was never any evidence of what or where the Princesses were killed or buried. One of the largest and most prevalent stories was that later on, many of the local Pomo Indians experienced visions of the two Princesses and often felt that there were Spirits nearby.

This mention of Spirits being envisioned made Clint really sit up and take special notice. Both John and Helen Adamson could see this immediate change in his demeanour. They could see this interest, so as the lunch finished and the conversation moved to the Pomo history of Dry Creek, Clint was granted unlimited access to their property. John and Helen did ask Clint to report any unique findings of his trek to where the graves were and the suspicions of the existence of the Spirits.

Clint left the Dry Creek Ranch and on his way back to Stonyford he started to think of how to make a thorough and cautious return back to the Dry Creek graves.

The next morning, after getting permission from John and Helen, Clint gathered some sandwiches, water and snacks in anticipation of his trip up Dry Creek. He also took a small calibre rifle. He loaded all the necessary provisions into his Jeep and proceeded to where a locked gate was near Dry Creek. John had given him a key so that there was easy access for entry. He then drove up to where the rough and narrow track became almost impassable, left his Jeep and decided to walk the rest of the way to his destination.

He was actually hoping that he would have no problem remembering the terrain where the gravesites were, or if they were still there.

As Clint ambled up the dry creek bed his memory started to kick in and he began to pick up some signs of long ago when he was a young man. At one point of his journey he stopped and observed a raised area near the dry creek bed. Here he remembered that he had stopped and spent about an hour or so scanning the small area for Indian artifacts when he was a young man. The area was a small Indian camp. Evidently it had been there many, many years. Maybe Clint was the only living person to know where it was, as it was overgrown with 'Buck' brush. Clint required a 'breather' so decided to sit down and have a drink of water near the old Indian campsite. While this was happening, he started to feel strange but nevertheless, positive feelings. At this point in time he knew this was the 'Spirits' that had always been with him since that hunting trip with Joe many years ago.

After a short and memorable stop Clint decided to keep moving on towards the old gravesites. The further he went, the more excited he felt as he kept receiving good vibrations and feelings. Clint could not believe that the Spirits were still with him and producing and releasing all these long pent-up emotions. It was like a strong warmth and glow emanating from within. Everything seemed surreal but as real visions appearing. All of these things seemed to be coming to a climax, when suddenly Clint strode around a narrow part of Dry Creek and then arrived at a clearing.

The Dry Creek gravesites were visible and just like Clint had remembered. He approached the raised embankment and sat, as close as possible to where Joe and he had rested from packing the buck many years ago. Suddenly, after all of these small events taking place, Clint began to feel an overwhelming tiredness. Everything in his body became drained. He had no energy and a physical weakness. While all this was happening the 'Spirits' started sending visions and started to communicate with him. He felt a strange and sad energy being mysteriously transmitted. He began to relax and focus on the gravesites. This is when the real story of Clints life and Spirit influence began to arise.

CHAPTER 7

Mini and Pearl were the daughters of Chief Jack Sharkill and his wife Kalo. Chief Jack and his wife were proud of their daughters, as they were extremely hard workers and were liked by the rest of the small tribal community of Pomo's. As Mini and Pearl grew older many of the young Pomo braves tried to catch their eye as they were very becoming and would make good wives. The whole Pomo tribe had always been peaceful and not warlike. The tribes' lifestyle was subsistence and happiness. But this all changed when the coastal Indians arrived one afternoon ready to trade their items of mainly seashells and obsidian for Salt. As the young coastal braves had completed their trading they wanted more. Mainly young Pomo squaws for their pleasure.

Mini and Pearl began the story of their abduction to Clint as he rested. These sad and distressing accounts were now filtering into his persona by some mystical means. Mini and Pearls horrible description depicted the Coastal Indians becoming very aggressive with the day's trading. Somehow, they had obtained 'firewater' and had drunk quite a large amount at the usual ceremonial feast. One thing led to another and a few of the coastal Indians forced a few young Pomo squaws into the surrounding bushes. More 'firewater', and things got out of control with several fights taking place.

Chief Sharkill eventually had enough and told the coastal Indians to leave immediately before things got out of hand. The coastal Indians reluctantly left, but not immediately.

Mini and Pearl had become the main focus of the coastal Indians. After a planned scuffle they lured Mini and Pearl aside and gagged and tied them up and silently led them away from the Pomo camp. The coastal Indians eventually detoured away from their normal travelling paths over the Goat Mountain area. They took a surrounding path up Dry Creek. Mini and Pearl knew in their hearts that things would not end well for them. They began to chant to their Spiritual God for survival, to no avail!

The abductors finally reached the location where Clint now rested, listening to Mini and Pearl. He was very agitated and started to feel pains all through his weakened old body. Mini and Pearl then related their last living minutes to Clint.

Mini, being the eldest sister, was trying to be brave and show courage for her younger sister Pearl. Even when back at their home tribes camp, Mini had always shown to be very strong-willed. Often, she had taken the responsibility of making sure Pearl was guided in the right direction when growing from youth to adulthood. As a consequence, Pearl adored Mini and looked up to her for strength and love. Sisterly love was in abundance between the two.

Being abducted was a horrible experience. Mini was trying to cope by showing resistance and anger towards her captors. This 'brave face' of Mini was making her captors extremely angry as they did not expect this resistance. The small band of coastal Indians travelled all night but did a lot of back tracking and used many tricks to try to conceal their trail. Eventually they ended up in the very secluded area of Dry Creek, still very drunk and abusive. They had been travelling by horseback and Mini and Pearl were walking or jogging behind their captors. When the Indians reached this site at Dry Creek, they tied their horses to the small oak saplings and then took turns at raping Mini and

Pearl. The coastal Indians were brutal and paid no attention to the girls repeated yells and screams. Mini kept telling Pearl to be brave and strong. But this was impossible for her. As Mini finally relented her fight, she also saw that Pearl was giving up.

Mini thought of her parents and also of Pearl, who she so loved dearly. Suddenly visions of the wonderful Spirit began to appear. The Spirit sent lasting visions of helping others whenever a chance arose. Mini knew this vision was being instilled upon Pearl also. Just before the girls were killed the Spirit was locked into their souls.

The coastal Indians buried the girls at Dry Creek and immediately made hasty tracks towards their homeland on the Coast, using many indirect routes over Black Diamond Mountain and Goat Mountain.

As far as legend had it these men had made good of their escape.

Mini and Pearl were never seen or heard of again. Their parents were left devastated and were never the same.

Mini knew both she and Pearl were dead.. Knowing they were now 'Spirits', they would help others or an individual if the occasion ever arose. Of course, this was the eventual happening when Clint and Joe stopped for a rest near their graves at the upper reaches of Dry Creek. Mini and Pearl could sense that Clint needed to be in their Spirit powers as he had felt their presence. They decided that they could be guardians of Clints life, so attached their Spirits to his soul so that they could assist and guide him through his lifetime. Joe did not become attached with Mini and Pearls Spirits as he had not felt their powerful connections.

This final communication and connection with Mini and Pearl meant a lot to him. The visions and guidance they had blessed him with now made some sense. The story that they had shown, now made him aware of what the future may hold.

Clint could finally feel a sense of relief easing from his tired body and soul. He knew his physical lifetime was beginning to come to a conclusion. He wanted to eventually instil the powers of the Mini and Pearl Spirits to another human being when the time was right. Mini and Pearl wanted this transformation to happen too. They wanted Clint to become a "spirit guardian" to someone he thought worthy of when he ceased living.

Clint thought long and hard about how to achieve this. He was aware this was a special power and wanted this to be accomplished after his final resting place was established.

CHAPTER 8

————⟫⟫⟫⟫⟫•⟪⟪⟪⟪⟪————

Clint was still in Stonyford when he became very ill. He was not sure whether the illness was caused from the toxic spraying when serving in Vietnam as a soldier or just plain old age. He was well into his seventies now. Clint was constantly tired and was quite sure death was very near.

On the last day before his death, Clint managed to get into his faithful Jeep and made the trip from Edith's cabins to Harlene's board and bat Rancheria home. When he arrived there was no one home.

At this stage Clints health was deteriorating quickly and he was becoming very ill. His entire body ached, but he still managed to make his way along an overgrown path to the oak tree behind Harlene's house. Clint wanted to say his last goodbyes to Joe and Bob Archenta. There were no head stones or markers, just a couple of old grinding stones and names carved into the trunk of the oak tree.

As Clint arrived at the tree he knew his 'time' was up and he began to weep. He could not remember the last time he had wept. The 'Spirits' were always able to control his emotions. They were not there to help him now, as he fell at the base of his dear lifetime school friends and Vietnam veterans' graves. As he fell his physical presence ceased to function. The 'Spirits' took over his soul. Clint would now wait until the time was right to release his newly acquired 'Spirit' to whoever was in need of his guidance and strength in the future.

After Clints remains were found by some of Harlene's younger relatives, he was interred under the old oak tree near his friends Joe and Bob Archenta.

Clint's 'Spirit' was felt by many people in the Stonyford area. The oak tree and graves were eventually made into an historical place of interest once Clint's story became folklore. The Stonyford inhabitants, in particular the Pomo Indians, often related happenings that they felt were visitations of Clint, guiding them.

CHAPTER 9

Clint never mentioned much about his own ancestry throughout his lifetime. After his death, a few locals did some researching and found out his family consisted of his parents, brother and two sisters. His father was of English, Welsh descent and his mother was of Paiute Indian and Spanish ancestry. Hence, the Native American aspect was probably where his strong belief in 'Spirits' was born. The Paiutes were located near the border of California and Nevada and his mother had lived on an Indian Reservation in Bishop, California.

The local researchers also discovered that there were also Noma Lakas and Pomo Indians during the early years prior to Stonyford's existence.

ACKNOWLEDGEMENTS

I would like to thank the following individuals for their support, editing and typing of this novel; your assistance has been greatly appreciated: Justine Franzoi, Pam Oakes and Allie Botting.

Printed in the USA
CPSIA information can be obtained
at www.ICGtesting.com
LVHW03073410123
760674LV00070B/1757